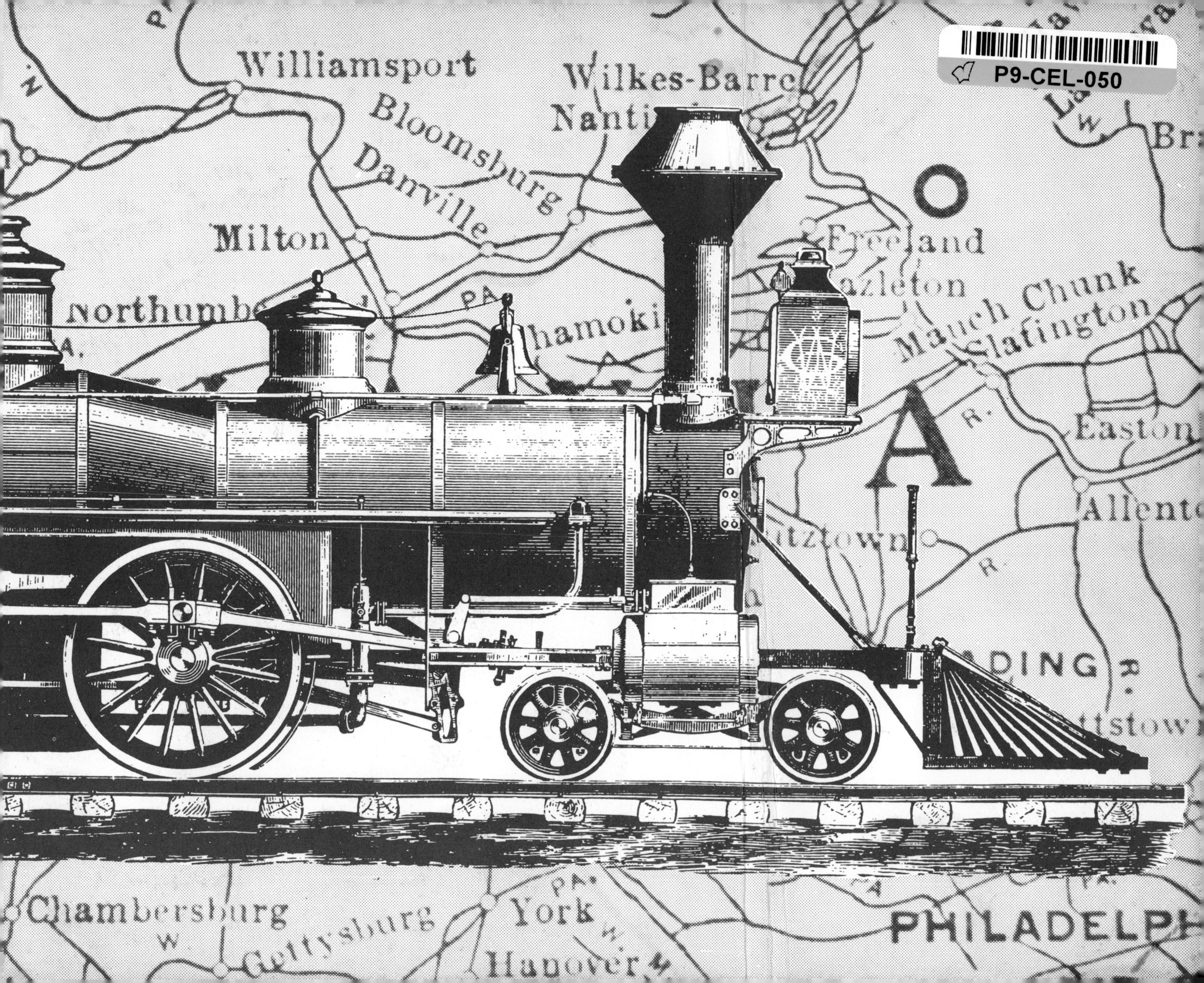
Williamsport
Bloomsburg
Danville
Milton
Freeland
Mauch Chunk
Slatington
Easton
Chambersburg
Gettysburg
York
Hanover